I Am Blessed

I Am Blessed

by *Grace Maccarone*

Illustrated by
Jacqueline Rogers

SCHOLASTIC INC.
New York Toronto London Auckland
Sydney Mexico City New Delhi Hong Kong

When morning comes,
I rise from bed
and shake the sleepies
from my head.

Before I'm even
getting dressed,
I count the ways
that I am blessed:

With two little eyes,
one little nose,

ten little fingers,
and ten little toes.

Water to wash with,

clothing to wear,

food to eat,

a playground to share,

with lots of other
girls and boys,
making lots of
happy noise.

With drums to beat,
with bells to ring,

with horns to toot,
and songs to sing.

When I go for a walk,
the time is best
to count the ways
that I am blessed:

With puppies and kittens,
butterflies and bees,

squirrels and birds,
flowers and trees.

My home sweet home,
my cozy chair,
my favorite book,
my teddy bear.

When nighttime comes,
I place my head
upon my pillow
in my bed.

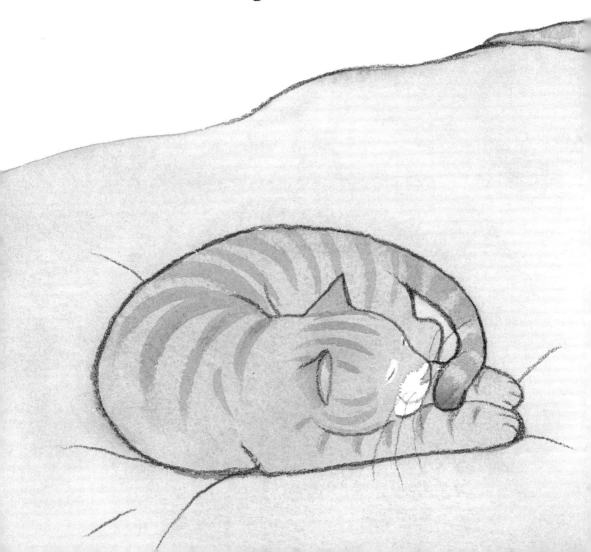

Before I lay
myself to rest,
I count the ways
that I am blessed:

With earth below
and sky above
and all the people
whom I love.

ISBN 978-0-545-39974-6

12 11 10 9 8 7 6 5 4 3 2 1   11 12 13 14 15 16/0

Printed in the U.S.A.   40

First Scholastic paperback printing, December 2011